STICKER PUZZLE BOOK
WILD ANIMALS

LONDON, NEW YORK,
MELBOURNE, MUNICH
AND DELHI

Designer & Illustrator Louise Comfort
Art Editor Sarah Crouch
Senior Editor Hazel Egerton
Managing Editor Maureen Rissik
Art Director Rachel Hamdi
Educational Director
Dr. Roberta Butler

This edition first published in Great Britain
in 2006 by Dorling Kindersley Limited,
80 Strand, London WC2R 0RL

A CIP catalogue record for this book is
available from the British Library.

ISBN 978-1-4053-1711-5

Colour reproduction
by Colourscan, Singapore
Printed and bound in China
by L.Rex Printing Co., Ltd.

See our complete catalogue at
www.dk.com

Where do they live?

Some animals live in cold places;
some live in hot places. Some animals
live in grassy places, and some live in
watery places. Find the stickers for
each of the four pictures and put
the animals in the right habitats.

2

3

Animal outsides

Each group below contains a set of objects that feel or look similar. For each group, find an animal sticker that fits that group.

Furry

Striped

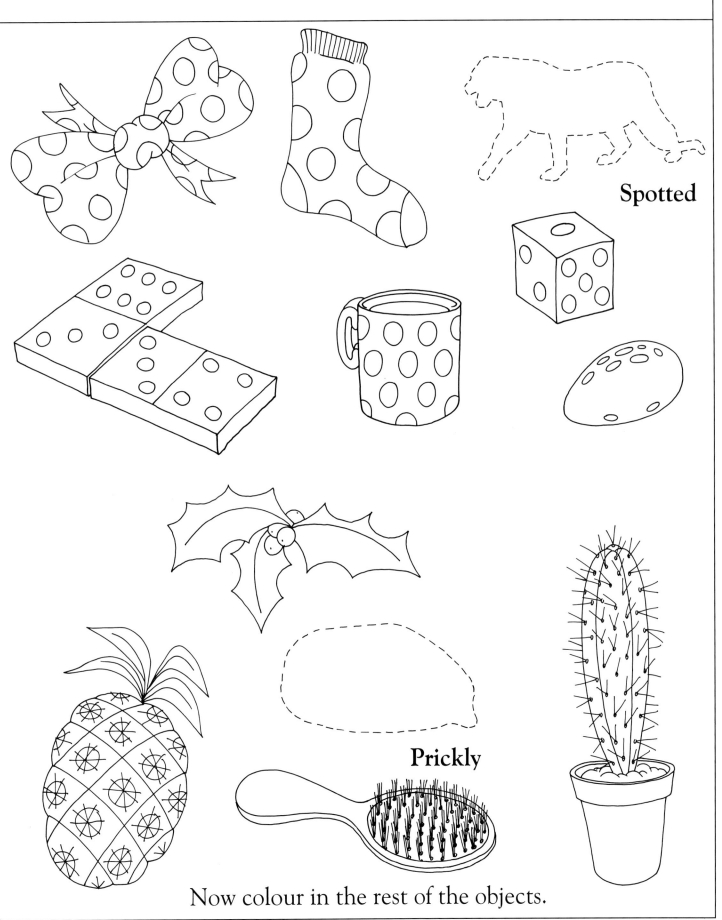

Spotted

Prickly

Now colour in the rest of the objects.

Amazing mazes

Help the spider and the otter to find their food. Place the right sticker on the dotted outline in the middle of each maze. Then use a pencil to trace the right path through the maze.

Stickers

Pages 2 and 3

Pages 4 and 5

Page 6

Page 11

2 2 4 7 8 4 8

Pages 12 and 13

Pages 14 and 15

Page 16

Use these extra stickers as you wish.

9

Legs and tails

How many legs do each of these animals have? When you have counted up each animal's legs, find the correct number-sticker and stick it on the dotted outline.

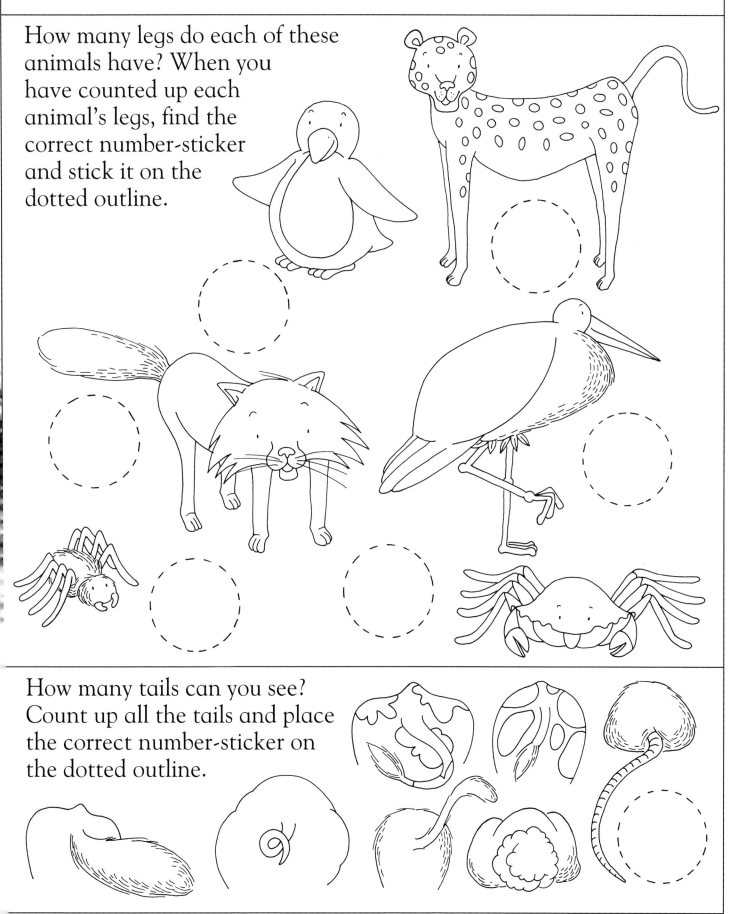

How many tails can you see? Count up all the tails and place the correct number-sticker on the dotted outline.

11

Spot the difference

These two pictures are not the same. If you look closely, you will see that the picture on this page contains eight animals that are missing from the picture on the opposite page.

First, find stickers for four of the missing animals and stick them on the dotted outlines. Now look for the other four missing animals and draw them in the empty spaces.

Now colour in the rest of the pictures.

13

Monkey business

To make counters, ask an adult to stick the monkey, gorilla, and orang-utan stickers on card and cut round the outlines. Find stickers for the animals lurking on the edges of the game board, then colour in the rest of the board. To play the game, you will need a dice.

Who will get to the coconuts first? Take turns to roll the dice and move forward the number of places shown. If you land on a tree, climb up to the square above. If you land on a snake, slide down to the square shown.

FINISH

46

34

33

18   19   20

17   16   15

START

1   2

GRRRR ...

14

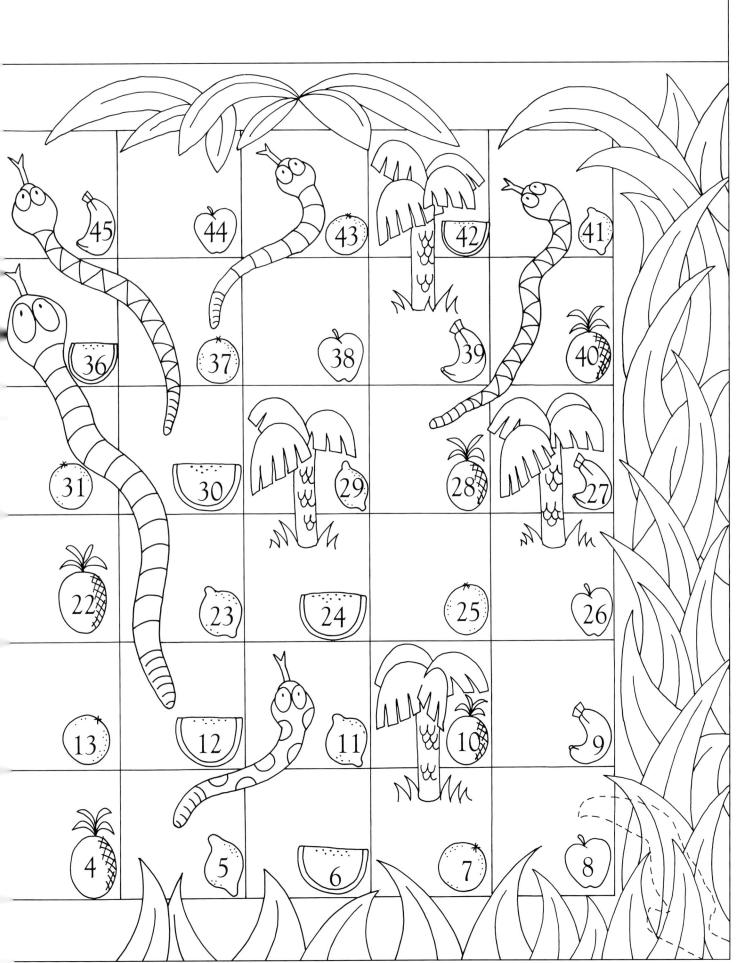

What's missing?

There are three animals missing from this garden: a bird, a butterfly, and a squirrel. Find stickers for the missing animals, then stick the stickers on the dotted outlines.

Now look closely at the picture. Find and colour in these animals: a mole, a beetle, a ladybird, and a snail.

Now colour in the rest of the picture.